Head for Home
Reading, Grade 4

Contents

Introduction

Learning to read is clearly one of the most important things your child will ever do. By the fourth grade, most children are confident, independent readers. They have developed a large vocabulary and have learned ways to understand the meanings of some unfamiliar words through context.

What is equally important for all readers, however, is reading with understanding. If your child reads a story but is unable to describe the events in his or her own words or answer questions about the story, then the reading loses its meaning. Young readers need practice to strengthen their reading comprehension abilities.

This book will help your child achieve reading success. The short stories are a mix of fiction and nonfiction. The stories are fun, and the one-page exercises are varied. Without feeling the pressure of a long story to remember or many pages of exercises to work, your child will develop a better understanding of the content and have fun doing it!

Helping Your Child With Reading Comprehension
- Provide a quiet place to work.
- Help your child to find the meanings of difficult words through the context of the story. Discuss the story.
- Go over the directions for the exercises together.
- Check the lesson when it is complete. Note areas of improvement as well as concern.

Thank you for being involved with your child's learning. A strong reading foundation will lead to a lifetime of reading enjoyment and success.

Putting It Off

"John," Miss Archer said in her strong voice, "you're a terrible procrastinator!" John's face turned red, but he was more upset than embarrassed. "You haven't picked out a book to read yet."

"How could she call me something like that?" he thought. "And she said it right in front of the whole class." He wasn't sure what a procrastinator was, but it didn't sound very nice. He was certain that he was not one of those, whatever it was.

"Did you hear what she called me?" John asked Melissa after school. "I feel like telling my mother. Can I use a word like that in front of my mother?"

"Well," Melissa sighed, "she said you are a terrible procrastinator. I suppose that's better than being good at it. Why don't you look the word up in the dictionary tonight and find out?"

The next day Melissa asked John if he had looked up the word *procrastinator.* "No," John said. "I was going to, but I didn't get around to it. I'll look it up later today."

"Well, I looked it up," Melissa said. "It means a person who always puts things off instead of doing them now."

"Oh," John said. "Well, I'll worry about it some other time."

1. John thinks that the word Miss Archer calls him is _____.
   Ⓐ a way of saying he is a good student
   Ⓑ not a very nice sounding word
   Ⓒ her way of getting him to use a dictionary
   Ⓓ a name for a person who reads fast

2. John is embarrassed because Miss Archer talks about him _____.
   Ⓐ to John's mother
   Ⓑ behind his back
   Ⓒ in front of the whole class
   Ⓓ over a loudspeaker

3. At first Melissa thinks that by calling John a "terrible procrastinator," Miss Archer means that he is _____.
   Ⓐ not good at procrastinating
   Ⓑ her favorite student
   Ⓒ a very careful reader
   Ⓓ very good at procrastinating

4. Miss Archer is saying that John _____.
   Ⓐ does not know how to read
   Ⓑ loses his temper easily
   Ⓒ always runs to his mother
   Ⓓ always puts things off

5. The next day, John proves that Miss Archer is _____.
   Ⓐ right about his being a procrastinator
   Ⓑ unfair to call him a procrastinator
   Ⓒ trying to say something nice about him
   Ⓓ sorry she says what she does in front of the whole class

Making the Grade

"Donna, have you done all your homework?" asked her father.

"Yes, Dad," said Donna. All except for her project, that is. Donna had a big project due the next week. She was doing a report on a famous American. She had chosen to report on the artist Georgia O'Keeffe. Other than choosing her subject, Donna had not done much work on her project yet. After all, she had until the next week.

Donna felt bored. She called her friend Trish. Trish was at the library doing research for her project. Then she called Sarah, but Sarah was out taking photographs for her project. Donna decided she might as well work on her own project. She began looking through her parents' collection of books for information. Then she used the computer to find more information. She found pictures of the artist and her paintings. Donna began to organize her information. It felt good to be getting ahead on her work.

The next day, Donna went to the library to finish her research. Then she bought a large piece of poster board and tried different arrangements of her pictures and information. For several days, Donna worked hard. She found that Georgia O'Keeffe was an interesting woman. Donna was enjoying herself.

When Donna finished her project with a day to spare, she was proud of her achievement. Her parents were pleased with the way she had worked, too. They had always told her not to wait until the last minute. Now she thought she knew why.

Donna gave her presentation and got an A. Her teacher said it was obvious that she had put much effort into it. Donna was very happy. She couldn't wait to tell her parents about the A she had earned!

Word List

| organize | spare | achievement | obvious |
| American | presentation | arrangements | research |

Donna had to do a project about a famous 1) _____.
She usually waited until the last minute to do her work, but she was bored.
She went to the library to 2) _____ her project. She began
to 3) _____ her information. She tried out different
4) _____ of her work on a piece of poster board. She finished
her work with a day to 5) _____. Donna gave her
6) _____. Her teacher said it was 7) _____
that she had put much effort into her project. Donna was proud of her
8) _____.

Directions Use the Word List above to choose the correct word for each meaning. Write your choice on the line.

9. a citizen of America _____

10. easy to see _____

11. to put in order _____

12. something done with great effort _____

13. left over, extra _____

14. careful study of a subject _____

15. things set in a certain way _____

16. something offered to a group _____

Can Do!

Maddie and Terese pulled the wagon slowly up the hill toward Maddie's house. The wagon had grown heavy with their collection of canned foods. The people in Maddie's neighborhood had been generous with their contributions. At first, Maddie and Terese had been hesitant to knock on people's doors and ask for canned foods. Everyone was nice, however, so the girls soon felt comfortable. Some people were not at home. A few did not answer their doors. But most people donated two or three cans. This trip up the hill was the second they had made that day.

The girls were collecting the cans for a school food drive. The class that collected the most cans would get a pizza party. The cans would go to a food bank that helped people in town who needed assistance from time to time. The bank had gotten low on food and this was a way to replenish its stores. Maddie and Terese wanted their class to get the party. Between their two neighborhoods, the girls collected 135 cans. Maddie's neighborhood had more houses, so they got most of them, 78 in all, from there.

Maddie and Terese added their cans to the cans the rest of their class had collected. There were 731 cans in all. The man from the food bank was amazed with the amount of food that the students had gathered. Maddie and Terese's class won the pizza party. They enjoyed the pizza, but they also felt good knowing they had done something to help other people.

Read each clue. Choose a word from the Word List, or do the mathematical equation, to find an answer to fit each clue. Write the words in the puzzle.

Word List

replenish   generous   contributions
hesitant   donated   assistance

ACROSS

2. gave

7. number of cans class had before Maddie and Terese added theirs (in words)

8. help

DOWN

1. something given along with others

3. number of cans collected from Terese's neighborhood (in words)

4. willing to share

5. not certain

6. fill again

Back to School

Have you ever heard anyone say something like this? "When I was your age, I had to walk to school. It was three miles each way. We walked in all kinds of weather. It was all uphill, too!"

Much has changed in education over the years. People may exaggerate how hard things used to be. But it is true that most students of today are fortunate when compared to those of long ago. There are many places in the world today where education is still a privilege. Many children stop going to school at an early age. Families need children to work and help with expenses. Some children go to school and work, too. To them, it must seem amazing that in other countries, until the age of 16 or so, a child's only responsibility is to go to school! Even in countries like the United States, free schooling for all has only come about in the last 100 years.

Early education consisted of listening and memorizing. Students did not often get books. Paper could be scarce. Students were required to memorize and recite long lists of facts. Classrooms were very different as well. There were no centers or group projects. Students stayed in their seats. They spoke only when spoken to. Or they paid the consequences! Only very recently has education become as interesting and exciting as it is today. Teachers try to motivate students to learn. They try to show students how what they are learning relates to their own lives. Classrooms are full of color, experimentation, and fun.

Today, there is still much for students to learn. The basics are still as important as they used to be. Our changing world also makes it important for students to learn and experience much more than reading, writing, and arithmetic. School has taken on a huge role in today's society. You may ride the bus, carpool, or walk three miles to get there. But be sure to jump in and make the most of your time at school!

1. This story is mostly about _____.
   Ⓐ schools long ago
   Ⓑ how teachers teach
   Ⓒ what students learn
   Ⓓ how schools have changed

2. What is a privilege?
   Ⓐ a gift
   Ⓑ a lesson
   Ⓒ a special benefit
   Ⓓ a mistake

3. Students of long ago did not often have _____.
   Ⓐ discipline
   Ⓑ books
   Ⓒ teachers
   Ⓓ schools

4. How do today's teachers try to interest students?
   Ⓐ by telling jokes
   Ⓑ by comparing learning to real life
   Ⓒ by making the work easy
   Ⓓ by making them memorize

5. How might a child from another country, who has not been able to go to school, feel about coming to a school in the United States?
   Ⓐ angry
   Ⓑ disappointed
   Ⓒ afraid
   Ⓓ happy

Far from Home

Laot Si's father taught at the university. When he came home to tell his family that they would live in the United States for a year while he taught at an American university, Laot Si looked dismayed. "What is wrong?" asked her father. "It will be most educational to visit another country, especially one that is so different from our own. You speak English very well, so you should have little trouble getting to know the people."

"I know, Papa, but it is such a large country, and what I know about the culture—the noise, the fast way of life, the cars—it seems frightening to me."

"It is not all like what you hear about or read about. I know that you will make many friends, and you will be grateful for the experience your whole life." Laot Si's father was not really confident about this, but he knew he should go. He wanted his family to be happy about the adventure, too.

They had not been in their new home very long, and a family from the university invited them to dinner. The daughter of the family was about Laot Si's age, and their fathers thought they might enjoy getting to know one another. They were both bashful at first, but soon the American girl, Jenny, was telling her new friend all about her school and friends. She asked all about Laot Si's country.

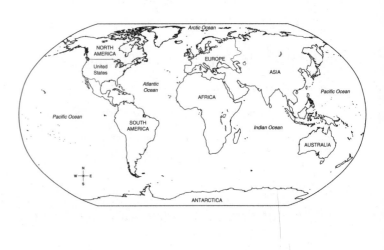

When the evening was over, their fathers asked the girls if they had enjoyed becoming acquainted. Jenny and Laot Si both laughed, a little embarrassed at being questioned in that way. Finally, Jenny offered, "I think we could probably write a book about how different our countries are."

"And," added Laot Si, "about how much alike they are, too." The girls smiled at each other because they knew they had made a friendship that would mean a great deal to each of them.

Read each sentence. Choose a word from the Word List that has the same meaning as the word or words in bold print. Write the word on the line.

Word List

culture	confident	educational
acquainted	bashful	dismayed

1. Laot Si's father said the year in America would be **something that would teach**.

_____

2. He was not **sure** that the family would enjoy their experience. _____

3. Laot Si was **made full of concern** by her father's news. _____

4. Laot Si and Jenny were **shy** at first. _____

5. They told each other about their own **country's ways**. _____

6. They were glad they had gotten **to know each other**. _____

Directions ▶ Write *true* or *false* next to each sentence.

7. _____ Laot Si did not want to go to America.

8. _____ Laot Si's father taught at a university.

9. _____ Laot Si went to Jenny's house for lunch.

10. _____ Jenny taught at a university in America.

11. _____ Jenny and Laot Si became friends.

12. _____ Jenny went to Laot Si's country to visit.

Space Place

Imagine that you and your family are moving to a space station for a year. How will your life be different than it is today? What kinds of changes can you expect? Astronauts have lived in space stations. They, and the scientists who study them, can answer these questions.

You may have already guessed one huge difference between living on Earth and living in a space station. Gravity is the force that holds us to Earth. There is no gravity in a space station. This is known as zero G. Astronauts have to adapt to zero G. They learn how to move around. They do this by gently pushing themselves in the direction they wish to go. Zero G has other effects on the body. The heart does not have to work as hard. It becomes smaller. People's legs become slightly smaller, too. Astronauts need to feel the pull of gravity occasionally. They need to get used to it again before coming back to Earth. Scientists have developed special equipment to help astronauts deal with this.

Sleeping in space is very comfortable. It has been described by one astronaut as the "world's best waterbed." But while they sleep, the astronauts' arms float out in front of them!

There is a feeling of separation in space. The astronauts can feel cut off from Earth. To make them feel more "at home," scientists have recommended lights that imitate day and night.

Astronauts in a space station wear regular clothing when they are inside. All their clothing is designed not to burn. When they leave the station, astronauts wear special gear. They must be protected from space and the sun. These suits are quite heavy. Together with the oxygen tanks and other equipment, they can weigh as much as 180 pounds! In space, however, the suits do not feel heavy. The astronauts can move quite well.

You and your family could expect to deal with all the same things that the astronauts do. Do you think you would like to live in space?

Read each clue. Choose a word from the Word List that fits each clue. Write the words in the puzzle.

Word List

| gravity | zero G | astronauts | adapt |
| effects | separation | recommended | imitate |

ACROSS

3. what one should do
4. space travelers
5. get used to
8. act like someone or something else

DOWN

1. results
2. keeping apart
6. force that holds things together
7. having none of #6

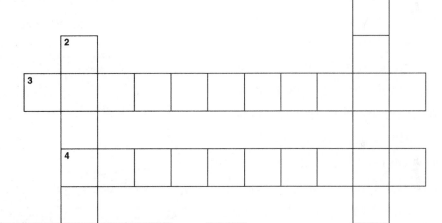

Families

Who is in your family? When you think of your family, you probably think of your mother, father, sisters or brothers, and you! There can be many other people in a family. Your grandparents, aunts, uncles, and cousins are all relatives. They are all a part of your family, too.

Years ago, most families lived in one place. Many people lived and worked in the same town all their lives. Their sons or daughters lived there, too. Children often built houses near their parents' homes. Younger people learned from older people. Younger generations could care for parents and grandparents as they got older.

Today, families often live far apart. Sons and daughters move away. Often they find opportunities for jobs in other states. Travel is faster and easier. Leaving home is less difficult, and people can fly home quickly. Easier travel has many advantages. But families have grown apart. Old people often live alone. They do not have the support they once had. It is easy for families to lose touch.

Many people write letters to keep in touch. They call on the telephone. Advances in communication help, too. People send computer mail. They send faxes. Staying in touch is important. It makes people feel close even when many miles separate them. Distance is only one of the things that have changed families. People of long ago would be amazed to see the families of today!

Word List

grandparents   relatives   generations   advances
opportunities   support   advantages   communication

ACROSS

3. people who are related
4. sending and receiving messages
7. help
8. your parents' parents

DOWN

1. chances
2. progress; forward movement
5. groups of people all born during a certain time
6. things that put one person in a better position than another

15

Too Hot or Not?

"How hot do you think it is today?"
  I heard my mother ask.
I looked at the thermometer;
  that was an easy task.
"It's seventy-two," I called out loud.
  "That's not too hot at all."
"Seventy-two!" she cried in surprise.
  "Oh! That's inside in the hall.
I want you to know how hot it is
  outside in the sun.
I was out there with our neighbors,
  and it's melting everyone!"
I hadn't been outside at all.
  (I just got up, you see.)
She's been out there and knows it's hot.
  So why does she ask me?
It must be very hot indeed
  to make our neighbors melt.
Did they drip like candles made of wax?
  I wonder how that felt.
"Maybe it's ninety in the sun—
  maybe a hundred and ten.
I'm going out to play," I said,
  "and I can tell you then."
I'll get too hot and start to melt,
  I'll play beneath some tree;
but how can knowing a number
  tell me how hot to be?

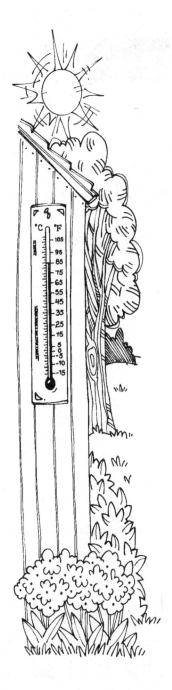

Answer each question about the poem. Darken the letter in front of the correct answer.

1. When Mother says that the neighbors are melting, she means that they _____.
   Ⓐ have all gone inside
   Ⓑ are feeling very warm
   Ⓒ are burning candles
   Ⓓ have disappeared before her eyes

2. It is seventy-two degrees _____.
   Ⓐ under the tree
   Ⓑ out in the sun
   Ⓒ under the covers
   Ⓓ inside in the hall

3. Mother was outside with the neighbors _____.
   Ⓐ talking about the weather
   Ⓑ lighting candles
   Ⓒ looking at the thermometer
   Ⓓ playing under a tree

4. The boy telling the story has just _____.
   Ⓐ been talking to the neighbors
   Ⓑ finished melting some candles
   Ⓒ gotten out of his bed
   Ⓓ come in from playing outside

5. The boy thinks that the best way to know how hot it is outside is to _____.
   Ⓐ ask the neighbors
   Ⓑ read a thermometer outside
   Ⓒ stay inside all day
   Ⓓ go out and see how he feels

Enough Gloves

Quinn was shopping in the department store when he saw a woman shaking her finger at the little boy. "He must have done something really bad," Quinn thought, moving down the aisle to hear what she was saying.

"This is the last pair of gloves I'm going to buy you this winter!" the woman said firmly, shaking her finger on one hand and a pair of gloves in the other. "I mean it! If you lose this pair, you can just go around with your hands in your pockets the rest of the winter!"

"Boy, she's really mean," Quinn thought, glaring at the boy's mother.

"What would you do?" the woman almost shouted at Quinn. "This is the third pair of gloves I've had to buy for him this winter! He had each pair a few days and then came home without them! He has to learn to respect things and take good care of them."

"Makes sense to me," Quinn said. And to tell the truth, it did, now that she had explained. "How come you're always losing your gloves?" he asked the boy with a nudge after the mother moved on down the aisle.

"Didn't lose any gloves," the kid said. "Billy and Roscoe had cold hands, and I knew their mothers couldn't afford to get them any."

1. Quinn moves closer to the woman and her son because Quinn _____.
   Ⓐ wants to know what the boy has done wrong
   Ⓑ is afraid that the woman will damage the gloves
   Ⓒ feels sorry for the woman
   Ⓓ knows the little boy

2. Quinn glares at the woman because he thinks she is _____.
   Ⓐ going to lose the boy
   Ⓑ not the boy's mother
   Ⓒ making too big a deal out of gloves
   Ⓓ going to say something very important

3. The mother is in the store to _____.
   Ⓐ find out what Quinn thinks
   Ⓑ find her son's lost gloves
   Ⓒ look for Billy's and Roscoe's mothers
   Ⓓ buy her son a pair of gloves

4. After the boy's mother explains, Quinn thinks that _____.
   Ⓐ she is a very mean woman
   Ⓑ the boy needs to learn a lesson
   Ⓒ the boy should have all the gloves he wants
   Ⓓ the mother should buy mittens instead

5. The boy does not have the first two pairs of gloves because _____.
   Ⓐ he lost them playing after school
   Ⓑ he felt sorry for his friends
   Ⓒ his mother gave them away
   Ⓓ he did not like wearing them

Mystery House

In Darla's neighborhood, there was a house that sat behind a high iron fence. It was surrounded by trees and bushes. The grass was often long and unkempt, but bright flowers grew in the window boxes. The roof needed patching and the porch sagged, but the windows were unbroken and clean. Darla heard many comments about the woman who lived there. People referred to her as crazy, scary, spooky, and all kinds of other things. She never seemed to leave the house, so Darla had no way of knowing just what the woman might be like.

One day at school, Darla met a new girl named Kim. Kim and Darla found that they had much in common. Darla invited Kim to her house that afternoon.

"My Aunt Nola lives on this street," said Kim as they got off the bus. "Let's go see her!"

As the girls walked down the street, it became apparent to Darla that Kim was headed straight toward the strange house! Darla was speechless as they walked up the overgrown path and knocked on the door. It was opened by a smiling woman in a wheelchair who invited them in and gave Kim a big hug. In the backyard, Aunt Nola wheeled down a ramp to the center of a charming garden where she had a table and some chairs. She offered the girls lemonade and cookies. An hour flew right by, and Darla hoped as they left that Kim would bring her back again soon.

20

Rewrite each sentence. Use a word with the same meaning from the Word List in place of the underlined words.

Word List   unkempt   speechless   unbroken   apparent

1. The windows in the house were **whole**.

_____

2. The lawn was **a mess**.

_____

3. It became **clear** that Kim was heading straight to the strange house.

_____

4. Darla was **unable to speak** as they walked down the path.

_____

Directions Choose the word that best fits each sentence. Write the word in the blank.

5. People _____ to the woman as crazy and scary.
    realized   referred   talked

6. Darla heard their _____.
    contents   thoughts   comments

7. The path was _____ with weeds.
    overgrown   overdone   cleared

8. The woman took them to her _____ garden.
    caring   vegetable   charming

Hats Off!

The hat had been given to Mrs. Beanwater many years before. It was the kind of pink that shows up a long way on a sunny day. It had a wide brim with little red cherries made of clay and a garden of tiny white flowers stuck in the band all around the brim.

The brim was a faded pink, even though the hat had always sat on a dark shelf. As soon as the friend who gave it to her left, Mrs. Beanwater sighed and said, "What a dreadful hat! What a frightfully ugly hat!"

The hat would still be on the shelf if it weren't for the crows. Mrs. Beanwater needed a hat for the scarecrow she made this summer. The friend who gave it to her had moved away, and Mrs. Beanwater was certain the hat would frighten anything that saw it.

As it turned out, the crows loved it; and so did Miss Dallywinkle. The crows sat along the brim picking at the clay cherries, and Miss Dallywinkle came to Mrs. Beanwater's door.

"Since your scarecrow's lovely hat isn't working," Miss Dallywinkle said, "I wonder if you might swap it for a hat of mine that I'm certain will scare the crows."

No one ever found out. Starting the very next day the townspeople began admiring a black felt hat that Mrs. Beanwater wore from that day on; and the poor scarecrow, who wore it for less than an hour, has gone hatless ever since.

1. When it comes to hats, Mrs. Beanwater and Miss Dallywinkle seem to have _____.
   Ⓐ too many for their own good
   Ⓑ a difference of opinion
   Ⓒ a liking for the same colors
   Ⓓ many hats with flowers on them

2. We do not know if the black felt hat would frighten the crows because _____.
   Ⓐ Mrs. Beanwater decides to wear it
   Ⓑ Miss Dallywinkle decides to keep it
   Ⓒ the scarecrow refuses to wear it
   Ⓓ someone in town steals it

3. Miss Dallywinkle offers to swap hats because she _____.
   Ⓐ thinks the scarecrow looks silly in it
   Ⓑ has given the pink hat to Mrs. Beanwater
   Ⓒ really likes the pink hat
   Ⓓ feels sorry for Mrs. Beanwater

4. The black felt hat is admired by _____.
   Ⓐ both Miss Dallywinkle and Mrs. Beanwater
   Ⓑ neither Miss Dallywinkle nor Mrs. Beanwater
   Ⓒ only Miss Dallywinkle
   Ⓓ Mrs. Beanwater

5. The crows in this story seem to agree with _____.
   Ⓐ Miss Dallywinkle
   Ⓑ Mrs. Beanwater
   Ⓒ neither Miss Dallywinkle nor Mrs. Beanwater
   Ⓓ the townspeople

Animals in Space

Animals have done many surprising things. Some have been heroes. Some have been stars in movies and on television shows. Animals help people in many ways. Animals have even helped people to study space travel.

Since 1957, many animals have gone into space. They have helped scientists answer questions about space travel. They have helped make space travel safe for humans. The first animal in space was a dog named Laika. She was the first Earth creature to orbit Earth. She showed that humans could survive space travel. Unfortunately, Laika did not survive her journey. She died when her capsule ran out of oxygen.

Since then, other animals have followed Laika's path. Almost all have been safely recovered. Scientists have sent four more dogs and several chimpanzees and monkeys into space. Of these, only Gordo, a squirrel monkey, was lost. His capsule failed to float upon landing in the ocean.

All of these animals have risked their lives to help humans travel safely. We have no way of knowing what they may have thought about their journeys. Maybe Enos, a chimp that orbited Earth twice in 1961, "spoke" for all of them. It is said that when he was taken from his capsule, he jumped up and down with joy. Then he shook the hands of the people who had rescued him. It seems clear that he was glad to be back on Earth!

Think about the passage you read. Then fill in the blanks of the following paragraph with words from the Word List. (Remember to use a capital letter to begin a sentence.)

Word List

survive	chimp	oxygen	unfortunately
risked	orbited	capsule	recovered

Many animals have **1)** _____ their lives to help people

study space. A dog named Laika **2)** _____ Earth in 1957.

3) _____, Laika did not **4)** _____. She died

when her **5)** _____ ran out of **6)** _____.

Enos, a **7)** _____, orbited Earth twice in 1961. Enos was

8) _____ safely.

Directions Use the Word List above to choose the correct word for each meaning. Write your choice on the line.

9. got back _____

10. went around _____

11. to live _____

12. an invisible gas _____

13. without luck _____

14. put in danger _____

15. part of a spacecraft _____

16. a kind of ape _____

Bedelia

Al could not remember life before Bedelia arrived. It seemed that the big, gentle dog had always been with him. Al could remember all the way back to his fourth birthday. He could see Bedelia then, sitting on the floor next to his chair as he opened his presents. He could remember his first day of kindergarten, when Bedelia stayed in the car and he went into school. He could remember the first summer in their new house, when Bedelia got a new house of her own out in the yard.

In Al's memories, Bedelia was always full grown. He never thought of her as small, although he knew she was once a puppy. She was always tall and slim, with flowing red hair. Even now that Al was growing, Bedelia was still a big dog. She was as high as his chest, and she could raise her head to look right at him with her wide, brown eyes.

26

Directions Answer each question about the story. Darken the letter in front of the correct answer.

1. Bedelia is a _____.
   Ⓐ person
   Ⓑ dog
   Ⓒ cat
   Ⓓ fox

2. Al is probably _____.
   Ⓐ a young child
   Ⓑ an adult
   Ⓒ ten or eleven years old
   Ⓓ an old man

3. Which of these best describes Al's feelings for Bedelia?
   Ⓐ dislike
   Ⓑ fear
   Ⓒ wonder
   Ⓓ love

Directions Write *true* or *false* next to each sentence.

4. _____ Bedelia was always full grown.

5. _____ Al took Bedelia into kindergarten with him.

6. _____ Bedelia had a house of her own.

7. _____ Bedelia had flowing red hair.

8. _____ Al wishes for a different dog.

A Cat for Company

Ever since she could remember, Elizabeth had wanted to have a cat. She had stuffed cats, porcelain cats with their kittens, pictures of cats, and books about cats, but she did not have a cat of her own. She asked for one at every opportunity, but there always seemed to be some reason why she could not yet have a cat.

Finally, when Elizabeth turned ten, her parents gave her a certificate good for one cat. Elizabeth was thrilled. The next day she went with her father to the local pet shelter to pick out a kitten. It wasn't easy. They were all so cute! Elizabeth wished she could take them all home. At last she chose a pretty kitten. It was brown with flecks of gold, a gold stripe on its nose, and one gold foot. She brought it home and named it Specks. From the beginning, Specks knew that Elizabeth was her person. She always slept on Elizabeth's bed and jumped up on her lap when she sat down.

Shortly after getting Specks, Elizabeth's family moved to another state. Specks made the journey on Elizabeth's lap, curled up on a pillow and perfectly content. Elizabeth was glad to have Specks at her new home. She had to make new friends and go to a new school. It was nice to have the same old friend at home to be her companion when she felt lonely. Whenever Elizabeth did make a new friend, she couldn't wait to show off Specks. Her friends all thought Specks was beautiful. She had grown into a petite but pretty adult cat. In addition to her gold toe and the stripe on her nose, now she had a gold patch on her chest, too. Elizabeth could hardly remember what life had been like before Specks!

28

Read each clue. Choose a word from the Word List that fits each clue. Write the words in the puzzle.

Word List

| certificate | companion | addition | flecks |
| petite | content | local | porcelain |

ACROSS

2. nearby

4. small bits

6. adding to

8. an official paper

DOWN

1. a hard white material

3. one who stays with another

5. happy

7. small

29

Ghostly Towns

They are mysterious, strange, often spooky, and sometimes beautiful. Ghost towns are the remains of once bustling, lively villages. There are hundreds of ghost towns around the United States. Some are on islands. All that is left of most of them are cellar holes, graveyards, and a few decaying buildings. The roads may be overgrown. The wells may be covered over. Without someone to point out certain sites, a person might pass right by them. What happened to these towns? Where did all the people go? Why were these towns started and then left?

Ghost towns exist for several reasons. One of the most common is changes in economics. Many ghost towns started out as busy mill towns or quarry towns. People came to the town to work in the mill or quarry. Then people came who set up bakeries, schools, and shops. Soon, there was a community. But perhaps the resource was used up. Or someone found a better stone to use. Then people stopped buying the product that kept the town going. Soon people began to move away to look for other work. When there were not enough people to support the small businesses, they too closed. Eventually, the town became deserted. Many of the towns that began in the west when people searched for gold were left when there was no gold to be found, or the mines were emptied.

Some reasons for ghost towns are less common. One town in Massachusetts started on a rocky area, inland from the ocean. It was put there partly as protection from pirates. Later, pirates were no longer a threat. People slowly abandoned the town. The town of Flagstaff, Maine, was not only deserted, but also buried under water. This town was flooded to make a reserve water supply for the electric company. The people were forced to move and their houses to be lost for the good of many more people.

When you visit a ghost town, it is interesting to try to imagine what life must have been like for the people who lived there. Often you can find out much from people who still live nearby. There are usually many local tales about ghost towns and some that only add to the mystery.

Think about the passage you read. Then fill in the blanks of the following paragraph with words from the Word List.

Word List

decaying	abandoned	economics	quarry
resource	protection	sites	reserve

Ghost towns are towns that have been 1) _____. Many

towns became ghost towns because of changes in 2) _____.

If many people in the town worked at a 3) _____ and the

4) _____ that was being mined ran out, people would have

to look somewhere else for work. One town was built away from the ocean for

5) _____ from pirates. When pirates were no longer a problem,

the people moved to better places. Another town was flooded to create a water

6) _____ for the electric company. All that is left at many

7) _____ are old and 8) _____ buildings

and graveyards.

Directions A fact is something that has actually happened or that is true. An opinion is what someone thinks, which may or may not be true. Write *fact* or *opinion* in front of each sentence.

9. _____ Ghost towns are mysterious, strange, often spooky, and sometimes beautiful.

10. _____ Ghost towns are the remains of once bustling, lively villages.

11. _____ Many ghost towns started out as busy mill towns or quarry towns.

12. _____ One town was put there partly as protection from pirates.

13. _____ It is interesting to try to imagine what life must have been like.

Castles

Castles can be grand and mysterious places. The high walls, the passages and walkways, and the murky dungeons make castles seem from another world. Castles were not mysterious to those who built and lived in them hundreds of years ago. They were home.

Castles were like small towns. The lord and lady had their family and servants. There were workers and soldiers. There were people who kept up the buildings. There were gardens for growing food. There was usually a village outside the castle walls. The village sometimes helped protect the castle. It may have had a wall around it, too. The village and farmlands supplied the castle with more food.

Castles were built for safety and defense from attack. There were several ways to attack a castle. For each type of attack, the castle soldiers had a plan to fight back. Walls were buried deep in the ground to prevent the digging of tunnels. Moats surrounded many castles as well. There were many small windows, cuts in the stone, and turrets. The soldiers could watch for and shoot arrows at their enemies from these places. They dropped rocks, boiling water, and hot sand onto their attackers. If the enemy put up ladders, they could be pushed away. A castle might be surrounded. This was so that no food could be brought in. The enemy hoped those inside would starve or surrender. Those in the castle made every attempt to keep large supplies of food on hand always.

Over the years, castles became less important. Times became more peaceful. Eventually, many castles were abandoned. Their stones were used for building in the surrounding villages. Many other stone castles still stand today. Some have been used as royal palaces.

Directions Answer each question about the story. Darken the letter in front of the correct answer.

1. Why were castles built?
   Ⓐ as a place for lords and ladies to live
   Ⓑ so that soldiers could practice fighting
   Ⓒ for safety and defense from attack
   Ⓓ to keep builders busy

2. Why would the enemy surround a castle?
   Ⓐ so that the people inside would starve or surrender
   Ⓑ so that no one could attack the castle
   Ⓒ so that the soldiers would see all the attackers
   Ⓓ so that they could see all the sides

3. Where did the people in a castle get their food?
   Ⓐ from visiting ships
   Ⓑ they made it all
   Ⓒ they grew some and got some from the village
   Ⓓ they bought it in cities

4. What might happen to a castle without soldiers?
   Ⓐ It would be kept safe by the villagers.
   Ⓑ The lord and lady could protect it.
   Ⓒ The enemy would be afraid to attack.
   Ⓓ The castle would fall quickly to the enemy.

5. How are some castles used today?
   Ⓐ They are still used for protection.
   Ⓑ They are mostly theme parks.
   Ⓒ Some are used as royal palaces.
   Ⓓ All of the castles have been destroyed.

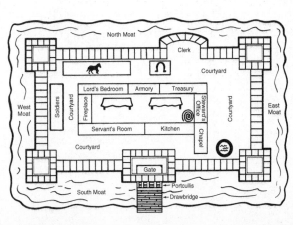

See Monsters?

Long ago sailors had much to fear from their voyages on the ocean. They did not know that Earth was round, so they feared falling off its edge. They heard stories of boiling waters. They heard of huge and menacing sea creatures. Many claimed to have seen them. Reports of sea monsters have not been completely explained away. People continue to see strange sea creatures.

Underwater monsters have been sighted all over the world. They have been seen by all kinds of people. Many people report very similar-looking creatures. They seem to fall into a few categories. Some are snake-like, but they do not move like snakes. Others have large bodies. Some have fins. Others have fish-like tails.

Many people do not believe these stories. They explain the sightings another way. They think people have seen giant squid or an octopus. They say that even seaweed beds or a school of dolphins can cause confusion. Other people cannot dismiss the stories altogether. They note that many of those who claim to see the monsters are intelligent, honest people. Many are seamen who know the water well. They know its natural inhabitants. Believers point out that these monsters could be related to prehistoric sea animals. In later years, people claim to have taken photographs. Could these prove that sea monsters exist?

Do you believe there are huge, strange creatures swimming in our oceans and lakes? As with many strange events, we may have to see it to believe it. That may be an experience some people would choose not to have!

34

Read each sentence. Choose a word from the Word List that has the same meaning as the word or words in bold print. Write the word on the line.

Word List

menacing	categories	dismiss	seamen
inhabitants	prehistoric	voyages	squid

1. **Men of the sea** and others have reported sightings of sea creatures for many years. _____

2. Their **trips on the water** were full of the unknown. _____

3. The sea creatures were said to be **dangerous**. _____

4. Sailors know the **creatures that live there** in the sea. _____

5. The creatures people see seem to fall into a few **groups**. _____

6. Some say that people are being confused by giant **sea animals**. _____

7. Others cannot **let go of** the stories that easily. _____

8. They believe the creatures may be relatives of **before the time of recorded history** animals. _____

Directions Write *true* or *false* next to each sentence.

9. _____ Sailors once thought that Earth was flat.

10. _____ They captured many sea monsters.

11. _____ People still report sightings of sea monsters.

12. _____ There is proof that sea monsters exist.

13. _____ People claim to have taken pictures of sea monsters.

A New View

An experience does not have to be very big or exciting to be an adventure. You don't have to make a grand discovery or travel far. You can have an adventure every day. Learning something new is an adventure. Exploring a new place in your town or neighborhood can be an adventure.

Every time you learn something new, it makes you grow. It gives you a new piece of knowledge that you can share with other people. How do you learn new things? When you are at school, there are new things to learn every day. Your teacher presents them to you in books, as class work, as research at the library, or as homework. When you are not in school, you continue to learn new things. You ask questions, you watch the news, you read books, and you go places. Sometimes you may go to a new place. Other times you may go to a place you've been to often. Each time, you can learn something new and make the trip an adventure.

Curiosity is what brings us adventure. If we don't wonder about anything, we will not experience much. If you wonder what is on the other side of the hill, you can go and find out. You may wonder what it would be like to try a new food, speak a different language, or live in another time. You can try the food, learn the language, or read a book. Museums are great fun to visit. They can teach us much about how other people have lived.

Every day of our lives is a day to learn and grow. There will always be something more to learn and do. There will always be an adventure waiting around the corner.

Read each question about the story. Darken the letter in front of the correct answer.

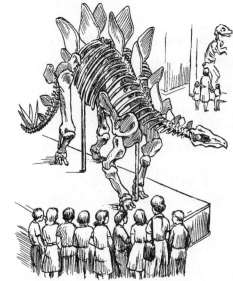

1. What is the main idea of this story?
   Ⓐ School is an adventure.
   Ⓑ Exploring is fun.
   Ⓒ Learning is an adventure.
   Ⓓ Reading is fun.

2. What is curiosity?
   Ⓐ wonder
   Ⓑ foolishness
   Ⓒ adventure
   Ⓓ learning

3. What does the story say that a person needs to have an adventure?
   Ⓐ a lot of money
   Ⓑ to travel far
   Ⓒ many friends
   Ⓓ curiosity

4. Which of these is not mentioned in the story?
   Ⓐ trying a new food
   Ⓑ learning to fly
   Ⓒ speaking a new language
   Ⓓ living in another time

5. Which of these is an opinion from the story?
   Ⓐ When you are at school, there are new things to learn every day.
   Ⓑ If you wonder what is on the other side of the hill, you can go and find out.
   Ⓒ Other times you may go to a place you've been to often.
   Ⓓ Museums are great fun to visit.

Movie Mystery

Jill and Paul went to the store to rent a movie. Jill was going to get some popcorn and Paul was going to choose the movie. "Remember, Paul," said Jill. "I don't like mysteries!"

When Paul and Jill met in front of the store, she said, "What did you get? Is it a good one? Were there many movies available?"

"Don't worry," said Paul. "It's not a mystery!"

They got to Paul's house, and Paul put the movie into the VCR player. There were many previews, and then finally the feature movie started.

"Oh!" said Jill. "Is this a good one? Have you seen this one yet?" As the characters in the movie came on, Jill said, "Who's that? I wonder what she will do!" or "I'll bet that man is the one who causes all the trouble!" Then, as the plot moved along, she would say, "Now why did they do that?" or "Don't they know there's a trap there? Why don't they go the other way around?"

Jill asked questions about every detail of the movie. Paul said, "Just watch!" The movie reached its climax; it was the big event that the plot of the movie had been working toward all along. Paul thought all of Jill's questions must have been answered. However, as the credits began to roll, Jill said, "Why didn't they just leave in the first place?"

Paul started to rewind the movie. He said, "Jill, I have never heard so many questions in my life! I think you might as well watch mysteries—for you, every movie is a mystery!"

Directions Read each clue. Choose a word from the Word List that fits each clue. Write the words in the puzzle.

Word List

available	previews	feature	plot
rewind	detail	climax	credits

ACROSS

4. to wind again
6. possible to get
7. a list that tells who did the work in a book or movie
8. the actions and events of a story

DOWN

1. views of something to come
2. the point of highest interest in a book or movie
3. in film, the main attraction
5. a bit of information

The Trunk

Amy and Andy crept up the attic stairs of their grandfather's house. He didn't mind if they looked around, but each time the children climbed the stairs, they felt a little frightened of the attic. Light came in at each end of the room through the windows, but the old crates, boxes, and furniture there gave the room a spooky feeling. Amy and Andy knew that most of the boxes had been there for many years. Still, something about the attic drew them there.

This time, Amy's eyes were drawn immediately to a trunk in the middle of a clearing on the floor. She did not remember seeing such a trunk on previous visits. Amy went to the trunk and opened the heavy lid. Inside were many odd items. Amy wasn't sure what they were. She reached toward the bottom of the trunk and pulled out a cloak. It looked like something a magician would wear. She put it over her shoulders.

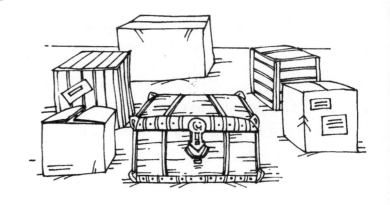

"Hey, Andy!" she called. "Look at me!"

"Where are you?" said Andy. "Amy, stop playing games. Where did you go?"

"Right here, silly!" said Amy. "I'm trying out this cloak!" As she took it off, she reappeared.

The children took turns trying on the cloak and decided it must be magic. They put it back into the trunk and ran down the stairs to tell their grandfather. When he heard their story, their grandfather laughed. The children insisted that he come up and look at the trunk with them, but when they got back to the attic, the whole trunk was gone! They looked all over the attic for the trunk, but they never found it again. No one but Amy and Adam seemed to believe their story of the cloak. But they couldn't help noticing a twinkle in their grandfather's eye whenever they told the story.

1. The children found the trunk in _____.
   Ⓐ their grandfather's cellar
   Ⓑ their grandfather's garage
   Ⓒ their parents' attic
   Ⓓ their grandfather's attic

2. The trunk was _____.
   Ⓐ something they had seen before
   Ⓑ something they had not seen before
   Ⓒ buried by many old boxes
   Ⓓ empty except for the cloak

3. The cloak made Amy _____.
   Ⓐ hungry
   Ⓑ shrink
   Ⓒ disappear
   Ⓓ hot

4. When they looked for the trunk again, _____.
   Ⓐ it was gone
   Ⓑ it was locked shut
   Ⓒ it had been moved
   Ⓓ it was empty

5. The twinkle in their grandfather's eye probably made the children
   think that _____.
   Ⓐ their grandfather was crying
   Ⓑ their grandfather was old
   Ⓒ their grandfather had a secret
   Ⓓ their grandfather did not believe them

Challenge! Find the Sentence!

In each puzzle, there are hidden words that form a sentence. The words go across or up and down.

Directions ▸ **Find the hidden words and write the sentence.**

T	H	E	Q	D	N	X	X	R	B
C	Y	T	M	W	A	L	K	E	D
E	Z	O	X	R	I	W	N	Y	O
J	K	S	T	V	S	C	B	P	V
N	P	E	T	N	L	A	N	Y	N
F	A	O	C	S	T	O	R	E	L
B	O	B	B	Y	S	Z	X	D	S

1. _____

_____

F	I	N	G	E	R	S
Y	G	H	U	C	B	Z
I	U	I	Z	A	N	D
P	D	S	O	Q	T	X
P	V	U	W	B	H	M
E	L	I	C	K	E	D
D	O	G	S	N	T	F

2. _____

_____

Three in a Row!

Directions Two players each choose a letter—*X* or *O*. The younger player goes first. The first player names and spells the homophone partner for a word on the game board. If the player is correct, he or she writes an *X* or *O* on that space. The second player takes a turn. The player who first writes three letters in a row across, up-and-down, or diagonally wins.

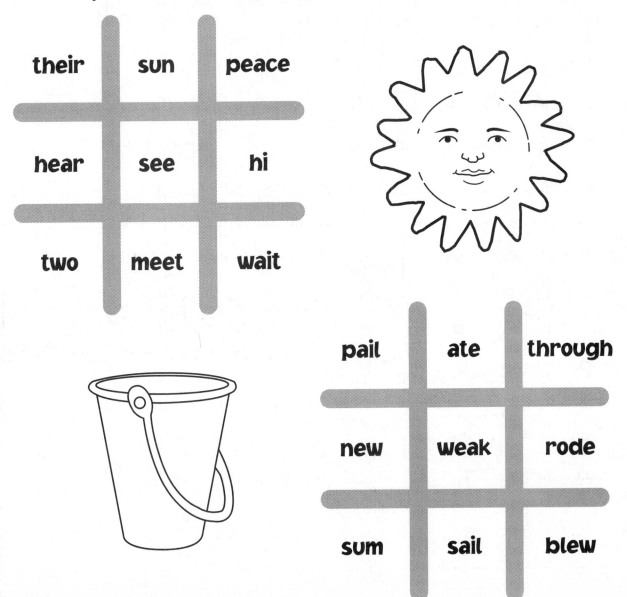

their	sun	peace
hear	see	hi
two	meet	wait

pail	ate	through
new	weak	rode
sum	sail	blew

Find the Hidden Picture!

Directions ► Color the words that are homographs. A picture will appear!

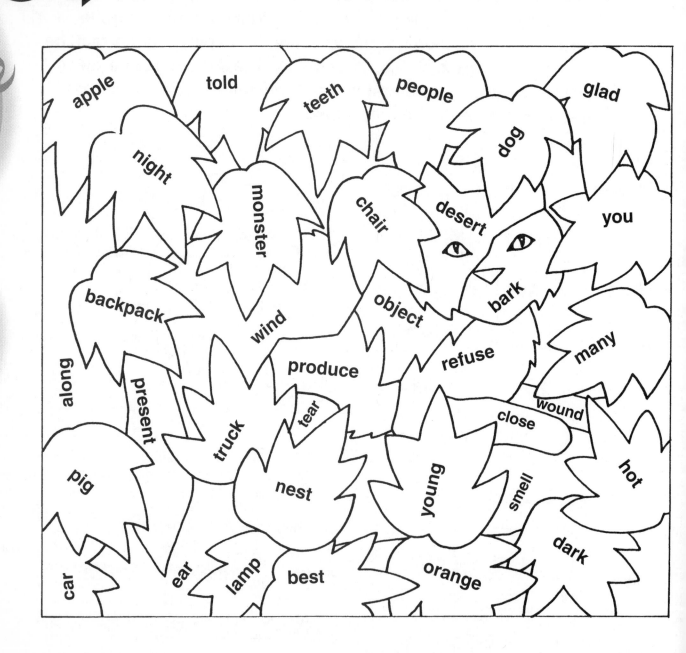

A-mazing!

Directions ▶ Draw a line from *Start* to the *Swamp*. Follow the path of words that name places having water.

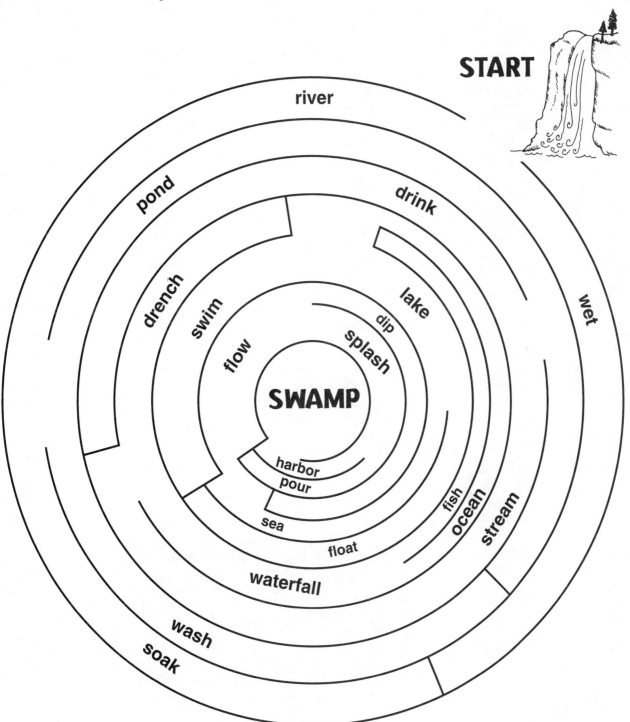

START

river

pond

drink

drench

wet

swim

lake

flow

dip

splash

SWAMP

harbor

pour

sea

fish

ocean

stream

float

waterfall

wash

soak

Congratulations!

This award certifies that

_____

is a Super Reader!

Head for Home
Reading, Grade 4

Answer Key

Page 3
1. B
2. C
3. A
4. D
5. A

Page 5
1. American
2. research
3. organize
4. arrangements
5. spare
6. presentation
7. obvious
8. achievement
9. American
10. obvious
11. organize
12. achievement
13. spare
14. research
15. arrangements
16. presentation

Page 7
ACROSS
2. donated
7. five hundred ninety six
8. assistance
DOWN
1. contributions
3. fifty seven
4. generous
5. hesitant
6. replenish

Page 9
1. D
2. C
3. B
4. B
5. D

Page 11
1. educational
2. confident
3. dismayed
4. bashful
5. culture
6. acquainted
7. true
8. true
9. false
10. false
11. true
12. false

Page 13
ACROSS
3. recommended
4. astronauts
5. adapt
8. imitate
DOWN
1. effects
2. separation
6. gravity
7. zero G

Page 15
ACROSS
3. relatives
4. communication
7. support
8. grandparents
DOWN
1. opportunities
2. advances
5. generations
6. advantages

Page 17
1. B
2. D
3. A
4. C
5. D

Page 19
1. A
2. C
3. D
4. B
5. B

Page 21
Sentences using the following
   words:
1. unbroken
2. unkempt
3. apparent
4. speechless
5. referred
6. comments
7. overgrown
8. charming

Page 23
1. B
2. A
3. C
4. D
5. A

Page 25
1. risked
2. orbited
3. Unfortunately
4. survive
5. capsule
6. oxygen
7. chimp
8. recovered
9. recovered
10. orbited
11. survive
12. oxygen
13. unfortunately
14. risked
15. capsule
16. chimp

Page 27
1. B
2. C
3. D
4. false
5. false
6. true
7. true
8. false

Page 29
ACROSS
2. local
4. flecks
6. addition
8. certificate
DOWN
1. porcelain
3. companion
5. content
7. petite

Page 31
1. abandoned
2. economics
3. quarry
4. resource
5. protection
6. reserve
7. sites
8. decaying
9. opinion
10. fact
11. fact
12. fact
13. opinion

Page 33
1. C
2. A
3. C
4. D
5. C

Page 35
1. seamen
2. voyages
3. menacing
4. inhabitants
5. categories
6. squid
7. dismiss
8. prehistoric
9. true
10. false
11. true
12. false
13. true

Page 37
1. C
2. A
3. D
4. B
5. D

Page 39
ACROSS
4. rewind
6. available
7. credits
8. plot
DOWN
1. previews
2. climax
3. feature
5. detail

Page 41
1. D
2. B
3. C
4. A
5. C

Page 42
1. Bobby walked to the pet store.
2. The dogs yipped and licked his fingers.

Page 43
First game: their/there, sun/son, peace/piece, hear/here, see/sea, hi/high, two/to/too, meet/meat, wait/weight
Second game: pail/pale, ate/eight, through/threw, new/knew, weak/week, rode/road, sum/some, sail/sale, blew/blue

Page 44
Homographs: desert, bark, object, refuse, wound, close, wind, tear, produce, present. Hidden picture is a cat.

Page 45
Path through maze: river, pond, stream, waterfall, ocean, lake, sea, harbor, swamp